TITLES AVAILABLE FROM LAGOON BOOKS:

Books can be ordered from bookshops by quoting the above ISBN numbers.
Some titles may not be available in all countries. All titles are available in the UK.

Murder
in
Manhattan

A *Mystery* PUZZLE BOOK

YOU ARE THE DETECTIVE!

Series Editor: Simon Melhuish
Editor: Heather Dickson
Author: Nick Hoare
Page design and layout: Gary Sherwood and Gary Inwood Studios
Cover design, photography & illustrations: Gary Sherwood

Published by:
LAGOON BOOKS
PO BOX 311, KT2 5QW, UK

ISBN: 1899712488

© LAGOON BOOKS, 1996.
Lagoon Books is a trade mark of Lagoon Trading Company Limited.
All rights reserved.

Printed in Singapore.

INTRODUCTION

You, the reader, are a detective. One of the best. Even the best, however, need a holiday, which is exactly what you had planned, until this dossier hit your desk. Any other detective would have ignored it until they had returned from their two weeks in the Caribbean, or their bracing hiking holiday, or whatever it is that you detectives do to unwind after months of crimebusting.

But there are several reasons why you can't ignore it. It is, after all, a very high profile case, the murder of Lisa May Rimini, socialite and gangster's moll. In addition to that, the officer previously assigned to the case, Detective Schwarz, is baffled, which makes you all the keener. Is this because Schwarz is an old friend and a trusted colleague? No way! Schwarz is a jumped-up, arrogant fool who has been your constant rival for acclaim and advancement for the past five years.

This is the golden opportunity to put him back down where he belongs and to win yourself a promotion. He's done all the leg work, you've got all the information you need to catch Lisa May Rimini's murderer by the end of the book. Each page you read should take you one step closer to busting the crime...

Index

USEFUL TIPS

- All the information *except the actual interviews with the six suspects* is 100% accurate. Whether or not it is relevant or particularly helpful is another matter.
- Remember that the murderer is not necessarily the only person who is lying. Other people may well have things they want to hide, which might turn out to be completely unconnected to the murder.
- The murderer acted alone. There may be conspiracies, other characters may suspect or even feel fairly sure who killed the victim, but no one knows for certain, apart from the murderer, of course. And your good self.
- The local police, in the form of Detective Schwarz, are fallible. If they weren't, they wouldn't need your help. Throughout the book there are times when Schwarz will assess the new developments. To stop yourself getting misled by these, and to make sure you are ahead of your rival, you should check your own conclusions before reading these.

A notebook and pen will prove invaluable, as soon there will be more red herrings flying around than on a windy day on the Hudson.

Remember we are all relying on you to bring the murderer to justice.

Good luck!

GOTHAM GAZETTE

Sunday 27 September 1952

Heiress Murdered
at birthday bash

by Andy Setithwait

ACTRESS and socialite Lisa May Rimini, widow of NYC entrepreneur Gianni Rimini, died suddenly last night while hosting a party in her Manhattan home to celebrate her 33rd birthday.

The cause of death was initially thought to have been cardio-respiratory failure, but police attending the scene interviewed several people and sent her body for an immediate autopsy.

Sources from within the City Coroner's department later revealed that cause for further suspicion had arisen and the police have confirmed that they are now treating the case as murder.

Mrs Rimini lost her husband in July in what was widely believed to have been a gangland killing. Mr Rimini, 57, was shot repeatedly by assailant or assailants unknown as he left the Napolitano Social Club, one of his many business premises in the city.

The couple were childless. Exactly who will benefit from the Rimini fortune, thought to run to several hundred million dollars, remains unclear at this stage.

HOI POLLOI

MAGAZINE

30 September 1952

LIGHTNING STRIKES TWICE!

SECOND RIMINI MURDER!

By Glenda Carson, Society Features Editor

THE CURSE of Rimini struck again on Saturday night, leaving Lisa May Rimini terminally face down in her birthday tiramisu. As Manhattan moved to the sound of a thousand crocodile tears, hardened gold-digger Lisa May, whose ruthless ascent from off-Broadway chorus lines to third richest woman on the island has been well-documented in this column, was laid to rest yesterday in the Rimini Parthenon, at the Forest Hills rest home, with full Mafia honours. Sorry, did I say Mafia? I wouldn't dream of doubting the frequent denials from both the Riminis and their attorney, controversial defender Clara Bensonhurst. All those guys in the funeral procession really did need to wear sunglasses, what with the mist and the rain and all. And old Gianni was just a nice guy who had a bit of luck in the restaurant and property business. Sure he was. And Jimmy Durante's going to be the next pope.

Scene of Crime Report 1

Date: 27 September 1952

Time: 01:42hrs

Offence: MURDER
Victim (if known):   Mrs Lisa May Rimini,
female, 33 years

Perpetrator: Unknown

Location: Apartment 25,
13th Floor,
Merriman Building,
1435, Park Avenue

Description:

Body located in lounge. Witnesses said that at about 21:55hrs on Saturday 26 September, the victim complained of feeling faint. Approx. two minutes later, victim stood up to go to bathroom, then collapsed. Unconscious but breathing when emergency services arrived, she died despite all attempts to revive her. Time of death given as 22:29hrs.

Cause of Death:

Colouring of face and eyes, together with muscle spasms and cramps before seizure suggest murder through poisoning. Exact source and type of toxins as yet unknown. (confirmation pending positive lab ID.)

First to Scene: (All below present
at time of death)

10

Possible Suspects:

Clara Bensonhurst (F) Age 47.
Legal advisor to the deceased.
No previous convictions.

Miriam Kowalski aka Mimi Colada (F) 35.
Friend and co-resident of the deceased.
Cautioned for soliciting 12/06/45.

Antonio Delgordo aka Tony "The Pro" (M) 39.
Chauffeur and aide to the deceased. Non-resident, but has own room in apartment of deceased. Numerous convictions dating from 1931. Two jail terms, notably three years in Rikers Island for aggravated wounding.

Lucy Westerheim (F) 44.
Neighbour (14th floor.)
No previous convictions.

Charles Crowhurst (M) 52.
Neighbour (12th floor.)
No previous criminal convictions, but three civil cases; one for tax evasion, plus one bankruptcy and a divorce.

Winford Thurston (M) 29.
Non-resident.
Two convictions for possession of narcotics.

Officer on the scene:
Detective A.F. Schwarz

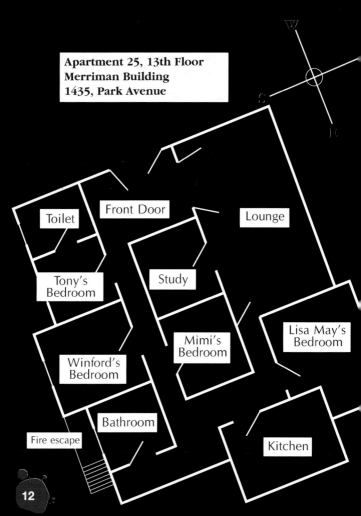

F O R E N S I C   R E P O R T

Laboratory:	Toxicology
Investigator:	R.P. McMurphy
Subject:	Lisa May Rimini (F), 33 years
Analysis:	Samples taken from the subject after time of death indicate presence of dangerously high levels of alcohol in the bloodstream, plus traces of various drugs, including the sleeping drug Somnulon. Cause of death seems to have been an overdose of a toxic substance. The pattern of rapid absorption suggests that the substance was administered orally, in solution rather than pill form, between one and two hours before subject's initial collapse.

27 September 1952

Mimi Colada:
Age 35 (real name Miriam Kowalski).

Second lead dancer at The Pineapple Lounge on
42nd Street, she is Lisa May's oldest friend in New
York. They met dancing in chorus lines in seedy
down-town clubs.

Lisa May met Gianni through Mimi,
who had been dating him for
about four months.
What progress Mimi has made
through the New York entertain-
ment world is largely thought to
have been down to the influence
and generosity of Lisa May, who
had insisted that her friend live
with her in the Merriman Building
apartment since the death of
her husband. They were
often seen out together
and their closeness caused
them to be frequently
mistaken as sisters.

14

Mimi contacted Clara Bensonhurst two days before the murder to see how much Gianni had put aside for her. At first Clara refused to divulge any information, as Gianni's will was to be kept secret until Lisa May's birthday on 26 September, but Mimi persisted and eventually Clara lost her temper and informed her, with great relish, that he had made no provision at all for her.

Tony "The Pro" Delgordo:
Age 39.

Driver for Lisa May. Previously Gianni's 'personal assistant', he has a lengthy and varied criminal past, but has 'gone straight' for the past seven years. Devoted to the Rimini family, he was with Gianni on the night he was shot and has worn black ever since.

The FBI suspect the involvement of Tony Delgordo in 13 unsolved killings over the past 15 years. Known as Tony "The Pro", which was originally a nickname from his days as a boxer but became a reflection of the zeal and professionalism with which he carried out any task put before him.

Lucy Westerheim:
Age 44.

Restaurateur and upstairs neighbour of the Riminis, she owns the Clarence Grill, Frankie's, The Bridge & Tunnel Club and The Pineapple Lounge. A self-made woman who hails from the same sort of rural background as Lisa May, she has built a thriving business, which was sufficiently successful to attract the legitimate attentions of Gianni Rimini. She is famed throughout Manhattan society for being hard-nosed and ruthless in her business dealings.

Lucy Westerheim has a reputation for ruthlessness. It is rumoured that she made the leap from manager to owner of her first restaurant by conducting a campaign of psychological warfare against her employers, an elderly Polish couple, who settled at a price way below the real market value and had nervous breakdowns soon after.

Charles Crowhurst:
Age 52.

The Riminis' downstairs neighbour, he married into
the Stoltz family, one of the most powerful banking
families in the country. The marriage collapsed, he
lost his executive position at the bank and set up his
own business. "Business" is probably too grand a
name for the chronicle of bad judgement, ineptitude
and bad luck that have dogged a series of ill-advised
ventures. He was interviewed by the police,
somewhat out of the blue, after the
shooting of Gianni, but was
released with no charges
and a full apology from
the Commissioner.

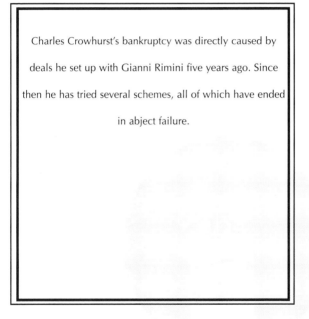

Charles Crowhurst's bankruptcy was directly caused by deals he set up with Gianni Rimini five years ago. Since then he has tried several schemes, all of which have ended in abject failure.

Clara Bensonhurst:
Age 47.

Attorney and legal advisor to Gianni Rimini for over 20 years, she is also famous for providing free legal support for the poor and oppressed. Despite countless attempts, Rimini was never convicted of anything while she worked for him. After his death, she undertook the management of his fortune, which she insisted had been intended for division between a number of New York-based charities.

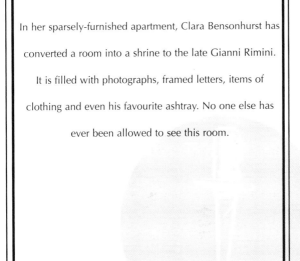

In her sparsely-furnished apartment, Clara Bensonhurst has converted a room into a shrine to the late Gianni Rimini. It is filled with photographs, framed letters, items of clothing and even his favourite ashtray. No one else has ever been allowed to see this room.

Winford Thurston:
Age 29.

Lisa May's lover. The latest in a line of beatnik poets to have been taken up by the chattering classes of Manhattan, Thurston rose to minor fame with the success of his first volume of poetry, "United States of Mind, Death & Beauty". He met Lisa May when she and Mimi visited one of the Greenwich Village coffee houses where he regularly performs and "hangs out". Although he is frequently interviewed and photographed in the communal Alphabet City squat he inhabits, he has been spending a lot of time in the Merriman Building apartment over the past few months.

Winford Thurston was known as "Dr Death" by his class mates at Westfield School, where he regularly poisoned laboratory animals for fun. He was the main suspect when half the school pack of beagles was found dead, but no conclusive evidence could connect him to it.

Detective Schwarz and Mimi Colada.

How did Mrs Rimini spend the day of her birthday?

We got up at about half past ten, had breakfast at Ronnie's Polish on 42nd Street, cos that's where we used to...Oh my god. I just can't believe it. I just can't believe she's dead, it's...After that we went shopping, and got back to the apartment at about 4.15pm. Then I had to go for my session with my chiropodist and Lisa May had to talk to that loser Crowhurst from downstairs. He'd been bugging her for ages, first to get her to look at something, then to make her mind up about it. He always pestered her with these stupid ideas. The guy's a nut. Harmless but real irritating. And then the rest all had a little while with her, wishing her a happy birthday, I guess.

Did anyone have cross words with her?

She had an argument with Winford, but that was fairly normal. He is quite a dark cloud when he wants to be. I imagine it was the usual marriage one.

Which is?

He's always proposing to her and then threatening to kill himself if she says no. She always said no but he always welched on his side of the deal. He's another nut. He's got this thing where he's convinced Tony is going to kill him. Later on he was trying to get back into her good books, filling everyone's glass with champagne like a little lapdog.

Did Mrs Rimini have a talk with Miss Bensonhurst?

That was the one Lisa May was really excited about.
Gianni's will said that she would find out how much she
was getting on her first birthday after his death. Lisa May
had like hundreds of plans, not just for the apartment, but
for businesses. Everyone says we're just a pair of floozies
with no brains, but in the months since Gianni's death Lisa
May has really relished running the business.

And was it good news?

Sure was! She'd been left complete control over the whole
of Gianni's fortune. That snooty Miss Bensonhurst spent the
rest of the evening looking as if she'd sucked a lemon.

Why would she feel like that?

Aw, she's one of those do-gooders. Gianni gave her a break,
but she feels guilty about taking...you know...Gianni's
money was a little dirty at times, so she does all this
bleeding-heart, civil-rights, help-the-poor stuff, just to
balance it up. She even convinced Gianni to move into
more and more legitimate businesses, you know, more
restaurants, less scams and jams. I don't have a problem
with that, and neither did Lisa May, but Bensonhurst was
kinda expecting to get a lot of Gianni's dough for her good
causes. I dunno, to set up a high school in Brooklyn or
something crazy like that.

What about Mr Delgordo?

Tony? What about him? Tony's always at the apartment.
Looking out the window, reading the sports pages,
whatever. I guess he kinda blames himself for what
happened to Gianni, but he'd never say anything though,
he's too proud. Recently he's hardly said a word to anyone.
Him and Lisa May used to be real tight, you know, cos
Gianni always wanted Tony to chaperone her everywhere,
but I guess in the past month or so they must've had a bust
up or something, cos they hardly ever speak to each other
any more. Sorry...spoke to each other. Oh my god... (large
sobs).

And how did you get on with Mrs Rimini?

We were like sisters, did everything together, shared
everything. I was her closest friend. People said we even
looked liked sisters.

You never argued?

Argued? Are you nuts? Lisa May loved me and I loved her.
We knew each other from way back, from before Park
Avenue, before Gianni, when we were both working the
small-time clubs. People can gossip all they want, but
nobody knew what she was really like, not like I knew her,
and nobody knew the bond we had between us.

Although not the only one to take it, Lisa May was the only person in the apartment to have a legitimate prescription for the drug Somnulon.

Detective Schwarz and Antonio Delgordo.

In your own words, tell me what happened on the evening of the 26th of September.

Simple. It was Mrs Rimini's birthday, she threw a party and she died.

That's all?

You bet. I'm just the driver. I didn't kill her, I didn't see nobody else kill her, she just collapsed, which she did from time to time. Only this time she didn't get up.

We have reason to believe she was poisoned. Did you see her eat or drink anything?

It was a birthday party, of course she ate and drank!

Was there any way her food or drink could've been tampered with?

Hell, yes. Miss Westerheim did most of the cooking, Mimi helped get things ready, Miss Bensonhurst brought the champagne, that creep from the downstairs apartment was passing her all her food. Even that toffee-nosed fake Thurston was serving drinks.

And what about you?

I told you already, I didn't kill her.

But could you have done so?

Sure. I was sitting next to her. I always did. Look, I know I've got a record, I know I've done some time, but Mr Rimini was like a father to me. He dies, he tells me to look out for his old lady. Where I come from, you promise a dying man something, you do it. Simple as that. So I look out for her, an' I drive her all over, 'cos after Mr Rimini goin' out like that, well, you can't be too careful.

You obviously weren't careful enough.

I did all I could. I even frisked all of the guests as they came in.

Why did you feel that was necessary?

Well, some of the people there, they were business before they were friends. Or they were friends who had come to Mrs R's birthday to discuss business. She'd inherited a lot from the old man and she was determined she was gonna do things her way, which put a few noses out of joint.

Any noses in particular?

Well, Miss Westerheim, all her restaurants were bought with a lotta help from the Rimini estate. Only now that business isn't so great, she's grousin' about a little increase in the interest payments. As for Crowhurst, he was always bothering Mr Rimini with a new scheme that was gonna make us all a billion dollars, or some investment plan of his. He's been hanging around Mrs Rimini non-stop for the past six weeks, asking her to reconsider something.

What?

Who knows? I'm just the driver, the hired muscle.

Who else do you think might have done it?

I dunno. That poet kid she was hanging around with, he was always kinda weird. I don't know nothing 'bout poetry, but all his stuff is kinda sick, not to mention all those freaks and low-lifes he hangs around with.
Mimi, she was like a sister to Lisa May...I mean Mrs

Rimini...and they used to fight like alley cats when the mood took them, especially recently, but I can't imagine she'd be able to plan a move like this, let alone do it.

And Miss Bensonhurst?

Woah, Clara and Mrs Rimini never saw eye-to-eye, but Clara's an attorney, for Chrissakes. She was devoted to Mr Rimini, she got him out of a number of close shaves and she wouldn't have done all that just so she could have a pop at his wife when he's gone.

What did they disagree about?

No idea. Like I said, I'm just the hired muscle. I don't know nothing 'bout the business side.

Before the party, what did you do?

Sat around, read the paper, watched the tube, you know.

Did anyone see you?

Er...yeah. I talked to Miss Bensonhurst, about baseball. She's a big fan. Talked for hours. We've known each other for years. From a distance, you understand.

Where did you do all this talking, reading and sitting around?

In my room. It's like a den, you know. Some nights I sleep there.

Did you leave before the party kicked off?

No need. Got everything. Ice box, mini espresso machine, the whole bit. Even got a bathroom in there. Man should have his comforts, you know.

While "the girls" were out shopping, Tony Delgordo

snuck off and bought himself a one-way train ticket to

Miami, booking a sleeper leaving that night at 02:30hrs.

Detective Schwarz and Clara Bensonhurst.

What time did you arrive at the apartment?

At about half past four.

And you stayed there all the time?

Yes. I had various things to discuss with Mrs Rimini, but I had to wait until she'd finished with Charles Crowhurst before I could see her alone.

Why was it so important to see her alone?

This wasn't a social call, you know. It was the first time I'd seen her since Gianni's funeral, and as you can understand, there are a lot of legal and financial matters when dealing with an estate of this size. I was quite surprised that Lisa May was celebrating at home, in such a frugal way. Usually she would have had it at the Waldorf or the Ritz-Carlton. Apparently Lucy Westerheim offered to take care of all the catering and then Mimi convinced her that it might seem a little tasteless to have a public celebration so soon after Gianni's murder. That someone so shameless should be worried about a matter of taste is quite remarkable.

I take it you don't approve of Miss Colada?

I was actually referring to...if Miss Colada and I have had our differences, it is only because I sometimes question her influence on the plans that Lisa May's making for the fortune.

Explain.

It's just that there is this huge sum of money, built up by a great man...

With all due respect, I think there are more than a few widows in this city who'd wanna argue with that.

There has never been any conclusive evidence to link Gianni Rimini with any sort of criminal. . . .

Save it, sister. The man in question is dead, now his wife is too. Stick to the story.

My only concern was that Lisa May wouldn't be true to her husband's vision. However questionable Gianni's beginnings were, he had, by the time of his brutal slaying, established a legitimate community-based business empire. It shouldn't just be frittered away by a couple of dancing girls playing at being society widows.

You're very devoted to your late employer.

Of course I am.

Did this cause any tensions between you and Lisa May?

My devotion was solely professional. And if you think that I spent twenty years defending Gianni in courts all over the country, just to kill the woman he loved, then you have severely under-rated my intelligence.

*Who said you were a suspect?
I'm just asking questions.*

Well, look, as the intermediary on the Rimini estate, I took the liberty of checking out Lisa May's associates. I bet I could tell you a thing or two about some of them.

You've been spying on all your employer's friends?

Look, all these people are either in business, or are going into business, with the Rimini estate, or stand to gain from Lisa May's imminent inheritance. I would have been neglecting my responsibilities if I hadn't done a certain amount of research.

Did you get a chance to ask Lisa May what she planned to do with the inheritance?

Er, yes, yes, I did.

How long were you with her?

About forty-five minutes. Until Lucy Westerheim arrived.

And how did Lisa May respond to your suggestions?

She...she gave my proposals serious consideration.

But did she accept them?

No...not immediately...she said she wanted more time. But we left on good terms and I was very optimistic about the outcome.

What time did you leave her?

About quarter to six.

What did you do until the party kicked off?

I, er, I sat and talked with Tony Delgordo. We're both baseball enthusiasts, you see.

The lawyer and the hoodlum, how nice. Did you do anything else?

I went into the kitchen, to get a mug for a flu preparation from Mrs Hendaya, but that was only for a second.

Two hours of baseball talk! I never knew it could be so interesting.

You'd be surprised, Detective. You'd be surprised.

And this was in the lounge?

Yes. Of course.

Clara Bensonhurst's only sporting interest is fencing, at which she was an internationally renowned women's champion and a feared opponent, famed for her speed and aggression.

Detective Schwarz and Winford Thurston III.

In your own words, tell me exactly....

I'd just like to say that I had nothing whatsoever to do with
this. Nothing at all. I was there, and I saw it all...I saw too
much...my fragile mind is still recoiling from the blow,
like a...

*On the night in question, I understand you had an
argument with Mrs Rimini.*

You understand nothing! How could you understand, you,
you cop, you faceless slave of oppression, you...

I take it you are resident in Mrs Rimini's apartment?

Of course not, you dolt! I am born of the streets. I do not
nest in the bourgeois underbel...

*OK, pal, by your own admission I can bust you for
vagrancy, which together with the parole agreement
on your last marijuana bust means you
automatically get three months in the city pen.
You've got a choice here loverboy. You drop the
bobo beatnik spiel and answer my questions, or you
get three months in the cage with the real people of
the street, capiche? Now what did you argue about?*

It wasn't really an argument. I was merely a little
disappointed when Lisa May turned down my proposal of
marriage.

*Apparently this was quite a frequent occurrence.
Most guys would've taken the hint by now.*

38

Deep down she wanted nothing else, of that I'm certain. She just needed someone to take her away from all that.

Away from what? Luxury? A life of leisure?

Away from hoodlums like Delgordo, and washed-up leaches like that hateful Colada woman. They were trying to take her over, trying to crush her spirit. I alone could see the true Lisa May. Marrying me was the only way for her to retain her spirit.

And of course none of this has anything to do with the multi-million dollar fortune she was about to inherit, has it?

I am an artist. Material wealth is nothing to me. You're also forgetting that I come from the Thurstons of Connecticut. My father is one of the top five richest businessmen on the east coast.

Earlier you called Miss Colada hateful. Why?

Because she was consumed with jealousy for Lisa May. She felt that everything that Lisa May had was rightfully hers, all because Gianni took her out a couple of times before getting bored rigid and picking up her friend Lisa May instead, as any sane man would. They only stayed "friends" so that Lisa May didn't feel guilty and Mimi could have access to a few of the things that she felt she had been deprived of. I'm no head-shrinker, but I think the jealousy was starting to drive her quite insane. Lisa May was paying for her to see an analyst, she's so pilled up she rattles when she walks. She even pretends she's going to see a chiropodist when she visits her shrink!

Were you in the apartment before the party?

Yes. I returned from lunch with Zane Darby, the editor of New Bohemia magazine, at about half past five. I went to bed to try to prepare for the party.

Did anyone see you?

No, to be honest, I was quite drunk, so I thought I'd better keep a low profile. I did see Mimi, pottering about in the kitchen, but I didn't say anything. I stayed in my room until everyone arrived for the party.

And apart from that, you didn't see or hear anything out of the ordinary?

No, I was dead to the world. The New Bohemia gives a very good... actually, it's probably nothing, it was probably just the booze, but I did wake up at one point, convinced there was someone walking in my room.
I thought I heard a door open and close and then footsteps. Whoever it was must've retraced their steps as I heard the door open and close a second time. It sounded so close that I got up and checked my door. It was still locked so I guess no one could've come in. Then I went back to bed. It must have been Mimi going into the bathroom or something.

Have you any idea when this was?

At 5.55pm exactly. I checked my watch. Then I heard a sliding noise. It must have been my mind playing tricks, I suppose. It's to be expected in my profession. A poet's imagination is his most important weapon, you know.

Winford Thurston's father has cut him off from the sizeable family fortune. He stands to inherit nothing.

Detective Schwarz and Charles Crowhurst.

I understand that you met with the deceased on the day of her death to discuss business.

Um, I live in the apartment downstairs, we were neighbours, it wasn't uncommon for us to talk.

So you just went up to borrow some sugar?

No. I'd asked Lisa May to consider a proposal, she'd told me she'd give me the answer on her birthday, so...I came up to hear what she'd decided.

What was the nature of this deal?

It was just a bit of property. Nothing really, particularly for the Riminis, I just wanted to buy something off them.

Where was this property?

Um, actually what I was after was the freehold on the Merriman Building apartment. I figured that, what with the inheritance and all, Lisa May would be moving out, getting something a bit more chi-chi, a bit grander. I own my own apartment, and a couple of others in the building. I thought, you know, I could get it at a reasonable price, then rent it out.

What did she say?

She was really enthusiastic, said she wanted to live on Fifth Avenue, or somewhere like that.

Did she give you anything in writing?

No, she said she was going to talk to that dragon of a lawyer of hers, but I guess she never got a chance. It was a terrible thing, a really terrible thing. So young, so much future...so much money.

Did you go home between talking business and coming to the party?

Yeah, never mix business with pleasure, you know. I left Lisa May at about five, went downstairs, showered, took a few calls, did some paperwork, then popped back upstairs.

Did anyone see you?

Only Tommy, who works the lift. He's always looking at his watch, got a memory like an elephant. Never forgets my birthday, he's...

Anyone else?

No. No one. Since Dolores left, I've lived alone.

Did you see anyone tampering with the food?

It was a buffet, you know, so everyone was touching the food, but then Lisa May served herself first, as she kept on saying she was the birthday girl.

I have it on good authority that you passed her most of her food.

Er...maybe I did. I was sitting next to her. You know, when one reaches a certain age, conducting business at the level I

43

do means that the old grey matter can get a little mushy when it's off duty, if you know what I mean.

What about the drinks?

Champagne. Miss Bensonhurst made a big show of insisting that we drank that big bottle of Cristal first, even though it was quite warm and Lisa May and Mimi had lots of chilled Krug all ready and waiting. Still, a superior grape, and all that. That cadaverous suitor of Lisa May's, Winford, ran into the kitchen to get the glasses and an ice bucket, then Tony poured them out, and gave them to people.

Anything else?

No, not that I can remember. Lisa May was fine, right up until about two minutes before she collapsed.

How long was this after her first mouthful?

About forty-five, fifty minutes. An hour at the most. She just said she felt really light-headed and we all said it was too much champagne, as a joke. Then she stood up and collapsed, poor thing.

Did you feel anything that could have been the effects of a poison or drug?

No, I don't believe so. I mean, it was all such a shock, it was difficult to say. That Tony Delgordo, he looked terrified when it happened, just looked up and started muttering, while Winford just couldn't stop staring, like...like...

Like what?

Like he was enjoying it, almost.

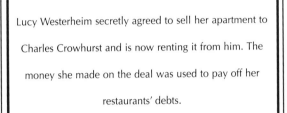

Lucy Westerheim secretly agreed to sell her apartment to Charles Crowhurst and is now renting it from him. The money she made on the deal was used to pay off her restaurants' debts.

Detective Schwarz and Lucy Westerheim.

I understand that you helped prepare the food on the night of the 26th.

Yeah. Well, no, to be honest I brought most of it over from The Clarence Grill, which is a restaurant I own on 2nd Avenue. It was a few plates of smoked salmon, a couple of salads, that sort of stuff. Lisa May was very careful about what she ate, you know.

Did anyone else help you?

Mimi sort of swanned around as usual, concentrating on what she kept on calling 'the presentation', but unless you call half an hour of putting four bits of parsley in place help, then no.

What time did you arrive with the food?

At about half past eight. I'd meant to get there earlier, but I'd had to check the accounts at The Clarence with the manager.

Did you tell anyone at the restaurant where you were taking it?

No, I just went into the kitchen, picked some stuff at random outta the fridge and the larder and brought it over.

At Mrs Rimini's house, did the food leave your sight at any point?

Sure. I left it in the kitchen, all covered up, while we had champagne.

Did anyone else go into the kitchen during that time?

Yeah, Winford went in to get a bucket for the champagne...

That Miss Bensonhurst brought?

That's right, a jeroboam of Cristal.

Did he get the glasses at the same time?

No, Tony went to get them a little bit later. Then Winford poured everyone a glass, and we did the whole "Happy Birthday" thing. After about half an hour I brought the food out. Then about half an hour into the meal, Lisa May collapsed.

I understand you borrowed heavily from the Riminis to fund your business.

Um.....yeah, yeah, that's true. Gianni was, um, very helpful, when I was starting out.

Is it true that you had recently fallen out with Lisa May over an increase in the interest she was charging you?

47

How did you...I think "fallen out" is...too strong a term. I confess that I found her decision...interesting, a little baffling even, given my long-term association with her husband...in a business sense, of course.

There are rumours that you are looking for buyers for at least two of your establishments.

Rumours, ha! This whole town is swimming in rumours. Times are hard, but the show ain't over 'til the fat lady sings. And I'm not about to kill one of my neighbours over a couple of hundred bucks. That's all I have to say on the subject.

Both Mimi Colada and Winford Thurston would test

positive for Somnulon, although neither has it on

prescription.

Detective Schwarz's Notes after initial interviews.

Bunch of creeps, any one of them could have done it.

Lucy Westerheim: suggested party at home, brought all food.

Motive: increased interest payments (sufficient?).

(TO DO: check food, check accounts).

Tony Delgordo: old-school hoodlum, weird reaction to death of

friend/boss, certainly capable. Style? Had fallen out with Lisa May.

Drinks?

(TO DO: check up with FBI & on argument with Lisa May. Drinks?).

Clara Bensonhurst: power-trip? Dislike of Lisa May? Fear of

losing control of fortune? Insisted on her champagne.

(TO DO: check on future of fortune, check champ bottle).

ALSO location of baseball talk?

Charles Crowhurst: creep, desperate, nervous in interview. Lied

about passing food? Who said he did? (TO DO: check passing of

food, check veracity of Lisa May "moving" story, check personal

history).

Mimi Colada: pathological liar? Very keen to point the finger at

Winford T., Clara B.,

(TO DO: check truthfulness of jealousy story).

Winford Thurston: fake, apparently unstable.

Keen to pour drinks. No material motive as yet. Spurned lover,

option of cash. Footsteps?

(TO DO: psychological profile).

52

With the recent covert acquisition of Lucy Westerheim's apartment, Charles Crowhurst now owns every apartment in the Merriman Building, except for the Rimini apartment.

Letter to Detective Schwarz from Arnold
Wilson, other partner in Clara Bensonhurst's
law firm.

Dear Det. Schwarz,

Lisa May Rimini recently asked me to take
care of her personal effects, due to some as-
yet-unexplained mistrust of Miss Bensonhurst.
On going through her papers, I discovered the
following letter, sent on the 24th September,
marked "To Be Opened On The Event Of

My Death".

Yours sincerely,

A. Wilson

Arnold Wilson

54

Dear Mr Wilson,

If I die in completely natural and unsuspicious circumstances, then please stop reading RIGHT NOW, and destroy this letter immediately.

If, however, there is anything violent or unnatural about my death, then it is essential that you know that I know that Tony Delgordo, my late husband's associate, organised my late husband's shooting. This action and related conspiracy had nothing to do with me. Mr Delgordo now knows that I know of his guilt, and, knowing the type of man he is, and knowing all too well of what he is capable, I now live in fear for my life. I repeat that I had no part whatsoever in the killing of my husband.

In the event of my murder, Mr Delgordo should be the number one suspect. He watched my husband, his life-long employer and protector, die on the sidewalk, and I am sure he plans to do the same to me.

Yours fearfully

Lisa May

Lisa May Rimini, widow.

Material supplied to Detective Schwarz from the archives of Clara Bensonhurst.

SPILLER & LANE, PRIVATE INVESTIGATORS

My partner John Spiller and I compiled this through access to various sensitive academic & medical sources, all of whom would be prejudiced by any revelation. The following material is presented for the eyes of Miss C. Bensonhurst and no one else.

Background on Winford Thurston III

Westfield School: Winford Thurston III expelled after attacking a janitor with a fire axe. Other notable offences included: leading armed assault on sanatorium, after which a teacher needed treatment for air gun pellet wounds, and two cases of cough liquor were confiscated; interjecting "unsuitable" poetry into school reading of Hiawatha on Founder's Day; sacrificed school pig to obscure Mayan deity. All of these were offences worthy of suspension.

Green Point Military Academy: expelled after using live rounds in exercise, wounding instructor and passing farmer in the process. He was found to have been hoarding weapons and ammunition in his room.

Sent by parents to the Thurrup Clinic, which specialises in adolescent disturbance. Here he was described as "morbid,

anti-social, obsessed with death, decay and mutilation",
"potentially dangerous, obsessive, with a tendency to
become dependant on people and substances", before
being expelled for selling stolen pharmaceuticals to fellow
patients.

Subsequent meetings with a number of NYC psychiatrists
established his main fear as that of being deserted, possibly
linked to maternal treatment in his formative years. Recent
success as a poet seems to have exacerbated the flaws in
his psyche.

Here is a sample of his work that particularly disturbed his
psychiatric counsellors.

Murder of Love
Beauty, a vulture, a vulture
Of blood, a vulture tearing
All that it loves. A vulture,
Murder, a vulture, love, drenched
In offal, drenched in blood,
Drenched in the love of murder,
And the murder of love.

A recent medical revealed extensive abuse of alcohol and
other substances, many of them prohibited, all of them
without prescription. Both his personal doctor and
psychiatrist have refused to treat him unless he submits to a
complete detoxification programme.

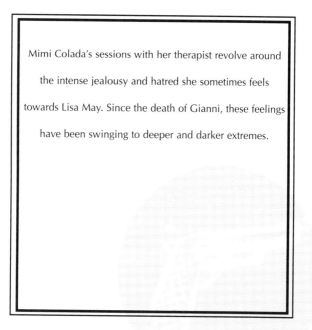

Mimi Colada's sessions with her therapist revolve around the intense jealousy and hatred she sometimes feels towards Lisa May. Since the death of Gianni, these feelings have been swinging to deeper and darker extremes.

Federal Bureau Of Investigation
Organised Crime Surveillance Unit

NEW YORK
2 October 1952

re enquiry on Tony Delgordo
from Det A.F. Schwarz, NYPD

We have been maintaining special Level 3
observation of Delgordo and the Rimini
household for the past four years. Level
3 clearance permits us to place
surveillance devices within the premises
designated on the permit, and on all
phonelines connected therein. We would be
happy to assist in any way we can with
your enquiry, in return for any
information, relevant or not on the
following subjects of investigation
DELGORDO, A, RIMINI, L.M, and
BENSONHURST, C.J.

Awaiting your response

Agent G. Brady Mulholland, 4123456

Lisa May:
...but you just have to live with it.

Tony D:
I don't believe you're saying this! You lied to me!
This was your damn idea in the first place!

Lisa May:
You're supposed to be the streetwise one, Tony, I'm new
to all this sort of thing ya know.

Tony D:
Don't play the innocent, Lisa May, you're fooling no one!

60

Lisa May:
Keep it down, do you want that slimeball downstairs to hear this?

(5 mins 14 secs of conversation are lost here)

Tony D:
I took a helluva risk for you. I risked going to the chair, I risked getting popped by any one of the New York families, not to mention betraying everything I believe in, and then you blow me out.

Lisa May:
Boo hoo, poor liddle Tony!

Tony D:
I betrayed the man who was like a father to me, for you! And now you blow me out for that snotty-nosed psycho Thurston, who's just after your cash.

Lisa May:
That's not true! But who cares, one peep out of you and I blow the whistle as hard as I can.

Tony D:
I'll take you with me, you goddamn gold-digger.

Lisa May:
You'll do nothing without my say-so. Face it, Tony, I got you where I want you. I can do anything I want with you, and don't even think about trying to get the better of me, 'cos I'm smarter than you, as your present god awful situation seems to demonstrate. Now go to bed, there's a good boy.

```
(end of audible conversation)
Federal Bureau Of Investigation
Organised Crime Surveillance Unit
```

```
Federal Bureau Of Investigation
Organised Crime Surveillance Unit

Confidential Surveillance Report

Subject:
Rimini, Gianni/Lisa May

Category:
Telephone tap, Rimini apartment

Date:
25 September 1952

B/ground:
Call between Lisa May and female, believed to
be Lucy Westerheim, calling from The
Pineapple Lounge.
```

Lucy W.:
Hi, it's Lucy.

Lisa May:
Lucy, sweetheart, it's been ages.

Lucy W.:
Yes, I haven't been down to your apartment since ... well
you know, Gianni died.

Lisa May:
My that is a long time and us being neighbours and all.
How are things? How's the diner business?

Lucy W.:
Well, to be honest, I'm calling about business. It's just that
there seems to be some sort of mistake, I'm sure it's just a
book-keeping error or something, on this month's
payment. Tony was round yesterday asking for eighteen
grand, which is two months' payment, I just wanted to
clear it up before...

Lisa May:
Oh, that's not a mistake. We had to double the interest on that loan, unforeseen circumstances and all. I'm sure you understand.

Lucy W.:
Lisa May, you just can't do that. We're struggling enough as it is.

Lisa May:
Look, I can do what the hell I want. I don't know what sort of cosy-cosy deal you had going with Gianni, the old man was probably soft on you, but now he's dead, and what I say goes. So pay up, or else...

Lucy W.:
Or else what?

Lisa May:
Or else I start to take your places as payment. You know the score, it's part of the agreement you had with Gianni.

Lucy W.:
Look, I can see you're playing at gangsters here, but at least they operate to a code of honour.

Lisa May:
Well, here's my new code of honour, give me my eighteen thou when you come to my birthday tomorrow, or The Pineapple, or one of those other joints of yours, is going to be under new management.

Lucy W.:
You can't just walk in and take them off me. Not even with your hotshot Bensonhurst paying everyone off.

Lisa May:
Well, if we can't, then maybe it'll be a busy night for the NYC Fire Department. See ya tomorrow, with my money.

Federal Bureau Of Investigation
Organised Crime Surveillance Unit

Confidential Surveillance Report

Subject:
Rimini, Gianni/Lisa May, Delgordo, Tony

Category:
Room tap, in chandelier, main reception room,
Rimini apartment

Date:
26 September 1952

B/ground:
Excerpt from Lisa May's birthday celebration,
present Lisa May, Tony Delgordo, Lucy
Westerheim, Mimi Colada, Winford Thurston,
Charles Crowhurst, Clara Bensonhurst.

Clara B.:
And I took the liberty of bringing you this.

Lisa May:
Clara, you shouldn't have. We've got bottles and bottles in the chiller.

Clara B.:
But we have to have this! It's the best, you know.

Charles C.:
Look, Lisa May, it's Cristal. It would be a shame to pass up such a rare opportunity.

Mimi C.:
But it's warm! You can't expect Lisa May to drink warm champagne on her birthday?

Winford T.:
It's OK, I'll get ice and the glasses.

Lisa May:
You don't know where they are, Winford!

Winford T.:
Yes, I do.

Lucy W.:
So how many candles will there be on the cake, Lisa May?

Clara B.:
Thirty-three

Lucy W.:
Thirty three? Is that all? I'd never have thought!

(Sound of cork popping and clatter of bucket.
Then champagne being poured)

Lisa May:
I think this is the first time I've ever seen you do anything helpful in this apartment, Winford.

Mimi C.:
Yeah, if you'd ever done it before you'd know that Lisa May always gets the frosted glass, not one of the normal glasses.

Charles C.:
Even I know that, and I live downstairs.

Tony D.:
It's only a glass, for Chrissakes. A glass is a glass. Don't mean anything. Don't make the champagne taste any different.

Mimi C.:
What do you know, Tony? I bet you'd be happy drinking it out of a paper bag on a bench in Central Park with all the other bums.

Charles C.:
I have to say, Tony, that that frosted glass flute stands out in much the same way as our radiant hostess does. May I propose a toast to the birthday girl? Happy Birthday.

notes

Detective Schwarz's Notes.

Tony D.: responsible for Gianni Rimini's death?; involved in Lisa May's killing? Why kill both?

Any connection?

Winford T.: nut, without a doubt: dangerous? Dangerous to Lisa May? Difficult to say with this sort.

BUG transcripts: Lisa May implicated in hubbie's death? Nothing concrete; makes for motive though.

Lucy W.: not just getting squeezed for a couple of hundred, something personal here.

Party tape: ambiguous. Everyone sticking booze, champagne and glasses under victim's nose like there is no tomorrow.

66

N.Y.P.D.

Criminology Laboratories

F O R E N S I C   R E P O R T

Crime Scene: Rimini Apartment,
Merriman Building, Park Avenue

Crime: Murder

Analysis: Tests confirm cause of death from
an overdose of Ricin, a highly
toxic substance obtained from
crushing the beans of a castor oil
plant. No traces of Ricin were
found in any foodstuffs on
victim's plate or in champagne
bottle. Victim's glass was empty at
time of death but traces of Ricin
found evenly around rim of glass.
Traces consistent with around a
teaspoonful of Ricin being added
to the victim's glass or the glass
being dipped in, or wiped, with a
solution of Ricin.

28 September 1952

A tooth-glass with similar traces of Ricin on it was
found on the window-ledge of the large bathroom,
next to a lush green castor oil plant, which had been
stripped of its beans.

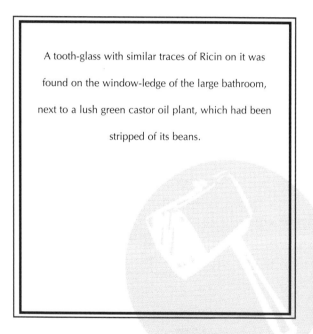

notes

Detective Schwarz's Notes.

After initial interview with Tommy Batherd, the elevator operator,

regarding comings and goings to the Rimini apartment.

10:30hrs: Tony Delgordo arrives.

10:45hrs: Mimi Colada, Lisa May Rimini

        & Tony Delgordo leave the apartment.

15:55hrs: Tony Delgordo returns.

16:15hrs: Mimi Colada & Lisa May Rimini return.

16:25hrs: Doctor Bowden, Mimi's 'chiropodist' arrives.

16:30hrs: Charles Crowhurst arrives at the same time

        as Clara Bensonhurst.

17.00hrs: Charles Crowhurst leaves.

17:30hrs: Winford Thurston returns.

17:35hrs: Dr Bowden leaves.

17:40hrs: Lucy Westerheim arrives.

18:05hrs: Lucy Westerheim leaves.

20:25hrs: Lucy Westerheim returns.

20:30hrs: Charles Crowhurst returns.

No one else came or went, according to Mr Batherd, until the

ambulance crew arrived.

Material supplied to Detective Schwarz from the archives of Clara Bensonhurst.

SPILLER & LANE, PRIVATE INVESTIGATORS

Dossier compiled on Charles Crowhurst's recent business manoeuvres;

First contact with Charles C. came when, acting under a general purchase directive from the Rimini estate, we heard of someone looking to sell property on Park Avenue. Made initial contact with Charles C., immediately became suspicious when property turned out to be the Merriman Building, including apartment currently owned by the Riminis.

Continued with initial stages of negotiation, without revealing true purpose of enquiry. After gaining Charles C.'s trust, we asked how he'd managed to secure so much high value property at such a low cost.

He revealed that, using a variety of methods, he had been making life unbearable for current residents. Methods included banging continuously on pipes (over a period of months), blocking drains, simulating "hauntings" by appearing on fire escape at night in horror costumes, paying local hoodlums to repeatedly mug the same people, even bribing police officers and town hall officials to harass them with fictitious complaints.

(Checked records & made enquiries: over the past two and a half years residents have been moving out, all of them thanking the "kind & brave" Mr Crowhurst for taking the properties on for them. All of them were extremely rich and happy to lose money in order to gain peace of mind.)

Charles C. admitted there was one property left, but assured us that guerrilla tactics weren't going to be necessary, as the owner, having come into money, would be moving upmarket very shortly.

We said we would consider what was both a very attractive deal for the buyer and an extremely profitable one for the seller, made our excuses and left.
Crowhurst seems to be a schemer, verging on the desperate, prepared to go a long way to make his margin.
We strongly recommend avoiding any business contact with this man.

Detective Schwarz with Lucy Westerheim.

I'm sorry for dragging you away from your business again. I guess you need all the time you can get your hands on at the moment.

Oh, things are tough, but they're not that bad, you know.

The reason I'm talking to you again is that there are a couple of things in your last statement that don't add up. When you were talking about the increased interest payments, you told me it was "a couple of hundred bucks", whereas sources have told me the monthly sum is now $18,000.

But that's not a lie! I didn't lie! It's just an expression.

But there's a big difference between $200 and $18,000. And, correct me if I'm wrong, but $18,000 seems a big chunk of change to be paying out every month.

You're forgetting I own four places; two restaurants, a bar and a club, and the turnover is fairly high. I know people paying out nearly that on just the one place. It's easy, miss a couple of payments, and you're in it up to your neck with some of these guys.

But $18,000 is a lot more than $9,000.

Twice as much to be exact. Look, I borrowed that money when I was managing two of these places and had a chance to buy in. Gianni was a regular, he liked me, and he stumped up the money. For three or four years, everything's fine, none of these horror stories about the Mafia guys getting a foothold and then steaming in and taking over. I paid the money to Tony once a month, and that's it. Gianni never tried to rip me off.

Then he dies and Lisa May starts throwing her weight around, right?

She, er she..I guess she didn't understand the finer points of the business. Either that, or she had some sort of grudge against me.

What would that be?

No idea.

You also came to the apartment earlier that evening.

Yeah, I told you that before, didn't I? I'm sure I did. I just...I went to talk to Lisa May, because there'd been a problem with getting the cash together, so I had to go and tell her that. That's all.

You didn't have an argument?

No...well...no. It wasn't particularly amicable, but...it wasn't an argument. Then I left.

You were there for more than 20 minutes. Is there something you're not telling me?

OK, so I had a few cross words with Lisa May. She was gonna take my livelihood, it was like she was out to destroy me. I asked her nicely to change her mind but she just laughed at me. Then it got a bit nasty. We'd had more or less the same conversation on the phone a couple of times in the past few days. I was kinda worked up when I left.

Where in the apartment did you talk to Lisa May?

In the study. She always did business in the office. She was trying real hard to look like a real businesswoman.

Did you go into any other room?

You have to go through the lounge to get to the study, but that was it.

Did you see anyone else in the apartment while you were there?

Yes. Clara Bensonhurst was coming out of Lisa May's office as I was going in.

There were minute traces of rust found in both the glass

in the bathroom and the frosted champagne glass.

**Detective Schwarz with Mrs Hendaya,
Mrs Rimini's home help.**

Tell me about the champagne glasses.

They very nice, very expensive glasses. They from Europe
somewhere, I dunno where.

Are they all the same?

They all the same shape, but one of them, Signora Rimini's,
is...is...it look like it very cold...

Frosted?

Ya...so. All of them were a present, from the uncle of Mr
Rimini, all the same, but two...how you say?...frosted.

What happened to the other one?

When Mr Rimini die, Mr Delgordo tell Mrs Rimini to smash
the other one, you know, like a...a ceremony.

Did you see them do it?

Who you think had to clean it up? Of course I see them
do it.

On the 26th, where were the glasses?

They were in the kitchen, in the cupboard, until I clean them.

When was that?

Just after the five o'clock, I am listening to the radio, so I know.

And did you clean them carefully?

Of course I clean them carefully! I wash each glass for two minutes, I rinse them in the clean water almost boiling, then I polish them until they are shining.

And then what did you do with them?

I leave them in the kitchen, on the sideboard, and I go to polish brass around lift door.

How long were they in the kitchen for?

I come back at about six, and I clean the plates and the oven. The glasses they are with me until the Mr Winford comes to fetch them.

When was this?

I dunno. I have to turn off radio when guests come. When the bottle is gone pop.

And no one touched them in that time?

No, I was there.

You're sure no one came into the kitchen while you were there?

Well, Miss Bensonhurst, she came, she wanted a cup and a spoon, for some medicine she had. So I get them for her.

And while you were getting these things for her, could she have touched the glasses without you seeing?

Well, it's possible, I guess, but she must be very quick, you know, like the lightning.

Letter to Detective Schwarz from Arnold Wilson, other partner in Clara Bensonhurst's law firm.

Dear Det. Schwarz,

Sorry it's taken me so long to get back to you. What with Mrs Rimini's death, and Miss Bensonhurst getting tangled up in the investigation, we have really had our hands full.

In answer to your query, neither I nor my partner are aware of any intention on Mrs Rimini's part to place the Merriman Building apartment on the market. We would normally be consulted in such a matter, though, to be blunt, Mrs Rimini was not a great one for observing the traditions and niceties of commerce. She was also much given to impulsive, spur-of-the-moment decisions, so such a decision to sell could well have been taken without her consulting us.

I trust this has been of some assistance to you. Please do not hesitate to contact this office with any further queries you might have.

Yours sincerely

A. Wilson

Arnold Wilson

notes

Detective Schwarz's Notes

Glass was source of poison

Lift man

Charles C.: complete crook, possibly deranged:

go as far as murder?

Lucy W.: on verge of losing everything to her downstairs

neighbour. Already lost her apartment.

Has lied/omitted throughout.

Cleaner: Who was in apartment between 17:00 and 18:00hrs?

Did any of them have a clear run at the glasses?

Detective Schwarz with Mimi Colada.

Who gave Lisa May the plant she kept in the large bathroom?

What the Castor Oil Plant? Loverboy brought it back from some trendy poetry reading week-end in Florida last month. Why d'ya wanna know?

The plant is an important piece of evidence in this case. Are you sure it was Winford who gave it to Lisa May?

Sure I'm sure, I live in the apartment too you know. Look ask anyone if you don't believe me. Tony was there and so was that loser Charles Crowhurst - he was always hanging around trying to get Lisa May to listen to another of his bum business de....

Okay, Okay. Now back to the plant. Did you notice if there were any beans on it?

Yeah come to think of it there were - loads of them and Winford specially told Lisa May to keep the plant in a south-facing room, where it would get lots of light.

Umm interesting. And did you go into the kitchen on the night of Lisa May's death?

Sure. I was helping Lucy with the food. She may run restaurants, but she knows nothing about dressing a meal.

2nd INTERVIEW

Did you go in before that, between five and six o'clock?

No. Not so I can remember. In fact I definitely didn't. You see, Dr Bowden was with me until about half five and when he left he gave me an injection that made me feel all woozy, so I just lay on my bed, for an hour or so.

Are you sure? It's just that I have a witness who saw you in the kitchen at just after half past five.

That's impossible. I was lying on my bed. Like I said, Dr Bowden gave me a ...

Is it common practice for a chiropodist to give a sedative injection?

Um...Dr Bowden's not just a chiropodist, he's more of a...an all-round healer. He was Lisa May's shr...doctor, too.

His name's on the prescription for Sommulon. Did you know she took it?

Oh, yeah. A couple of weeks ago Bowden came to see her, cos she'd been having terrible dreams and not sleeping and being bad-tempered, and the moment he left, she came out to the lounge where we were having drinks, and started offering them round, like they were candy.

Who else was there?

Me and Tony. He wasn't interested. Winford got in on the act soon after, though. He's crazy about anything like that, anything that makes you feel weird or kooky.

So you didn't go to the kitchen?

No, I just lay there. Not sleeping, just...relaxing.

Did you hear anything strange while you were just lying there?

Well yeah, now that you mention it, I'd been lying there for about 30 minutes when I heard some weird scuffling sounds coming out of a room nearby, either the bathroom or Winford's room.

Can you describe the noise?

It was a sort of muffled, scraping noise, like someone moving something heavy, or something that didn't want to move. Perhaps a sash window being forced open, I dunno. Then I heard someone stumbling around, like you know when someone's real clumsy and they're trying to be really quiet mixed with some other distant noises which were, yeah that's it, like they were from the street.

You realise I can check all this with this guy Bowden. Are you sure there's nothing else you need to tell me?

No, I can remember it all really clearly. I was just lying there and it was cold. Yes it seemed very cold that night............

(Interview terminated.)

Dear Detective Schwarz,

Firstly I feel I must object in principle to your approaches to myself and my practice. Your requests are most unethical, as are your methods. My receptionist, Miss Kinkladze, has had to ask me for counselling as a result of your phone call. However, I understand that one of my patients could be assisted by my co-operation and so I choose to ignore your bullying approach and give you the answers you so rudely demanded.

I did indeed visit Miss Colada on the day in question, arriving promptly for a 4.30pm appointment. I am not prepared to divulge any details of the session. Before leaving, I intravenously administered a powerful muscle-relaxant to help with the patient's critical anxiety. Previous observed administrations of the same dosage allow me to say with a degree of certainty that for the following hour or so the patient would have been conscious yet incapable of any movement other than breathing, blinking, swallowing, and slight head movements. I then left the premises at approximately 5.30pm.

As I have nothing more to say on the matter, any further queries will be forwarded to my attorney.

Emmet Bowden

M. Emmet Bowden

Detective Schwarz with Clara Bensonhurst.

I've got a problem with your story.

I thought you might have.

You know what I'm talking about? Your little sporting tête-à-tête with that fine upstanding member of the community Antonio Delgordo?

We did talk about baseball...

So you say, and frankly I don't give a damn whether it was baseball, field hockey, darts or whatever. The problem I have is with the location of your conversation.

The location?

Yeah, you said it was in the lounge, but good ol' Tony said it was in his den. So whadda you say to that?

Oh, Tony. Poor dumb Tony.

So what's the story?

When I finished talking with Lisa May...

What time was that, again?

About five forty-five. Tony grabbed me the moment I

emerged, said he had to talk to me and he practically dragged me into his room and shut the door.

Was this some kinda love thing going on?

Of course not!

Just asking!

The moment the door was shut, Tony broke down. He was almost crying, and shivering. He was like a trapped animal. He begged me to help him.

What was his problem?

He wouldn't say, said he could never tell me. He'd done something, something really bad, and he needed me to show him out the back door.

I'm sorry?

Occasionally when the FBI or the police thought they had something on one of Gianni's employees, or were trying to set someone up, we would have to make certain....arrangements to help them leave the country.

So what sort of arrangements did Tony want?

A false passport and an address in Sicily.

And you were prepared to do this for him without knowing why he had to leave?

I tried to get him to tell me, but...at the end of the day, I've known him for years, and I trust him.

So why did you lie, in the light of what happened?

He loved Lisa May, would've done anything for her. When he came to me he was desperate. Anyway, he couldn't have done it. As I was leaving Lisa May, Tony was coming in the front door. He didn't trust the phones in the apartment, and he'd had to make some preparations.

That doesn't tally with what the Batherd lift guy said.

Ha, Tony told me about that. He'd given the guy $500 to keep quiet and had threatened to send him down to the basement without his precious lift if he said anything. Tommy's a great guy, but you'd have to be crazy to argue with Tony in that sort of mood. But then Lisa May gets murdered, and you interview Tommy before Tony gets a chance to tell him to tell the truth. He guessed it was probably better to stick with the lie, to avoid suspicion. If you don't believe me ask Tommy. The poor guy's terrified. Been working here thirty-one years and the only stress he gets is if the cleaners don't vacuum his lift twice a day.

So you were with Tony from the point when he entered the apartment until when?

About seven I guess. I popped out at about six-thirty I think, to make Tony a cold cure drink, just to clear his head. But I don't think he left the room. He certainly couldn't have gone to the kitchen, cos I was there, or the bathroom, because I'd've seen him.

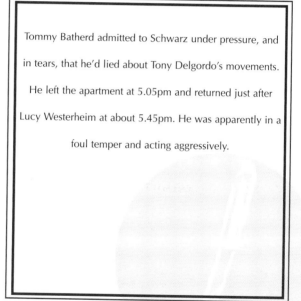

Tommy Batherd admitted to Schwarz under pressure, and in tears, that he'd lied about Tony Delgordo's movements. He left the apartment at 5.05pm and returned just after Lucy Westerheim at about 5.45pm. He was apparently in a foul temper and acting aggressively.

notes

Detective Schwarz's Notes.

Weird noise; figment of Winford T's intoxicated mind;

if not, what?

Noises from outside - window opening?

Which room?

Who knew about plant?

Killer certain of which glass to hit.

Access is the key............

CONCLUSION

You have by now been given all the information needed to identify the killer.

Do you know who it is?

Take your time, go over your notes, and think it through.

When you're sure you've solved this foul crime, turn the page and see if you are correct!

(The first solution page is in mirror-writing, to stop an accidental glance ruining the book - hold the book up to a mirror when you turn the page, and all will be revealed!)

DON'T TURN THE PAGE-

unless you want to know the solution!

SOLUTION

Charles Crowhurst was the murderer.

His motive: Crowhurst blamed Gianni Rimini for the failure
of his many business ventures. Buying up the Merriman
Building, bit by bit, was his last ditch attempt to make a
success of himself. So when Lisa May's refusal to sell her
apartment was the only obstacle between him and his goal,
he had no qualms about escalating his crazed tenant-
harassing antics to murder.

He was lying when he said he showered, took a few calls
and did some paperwork between leaving Lisa May's
apartment at 4.55pm and returning at 8.30pm.

Instead, he clambered up the rusty old fire escape to the
13th Floor and entered Lisa May's apartment via the
bathroom window. Once inside the bathroom, he grabbed a
handful of the castor oil plant's beans, ground them in the
garlic press he had carried up with him from his apartment
and dissolved the crushed pulp in a little water in a tooth-
glass he found in the bathroom.

Having mixed his poisonous potion, he then tip-toed from
the bathroom into the kitchen - taking care to close the
bathroom door behind him. Once inside the kitchen, he
sloshed enough of the clear, odourless liquid round the rim
of Lisa May's frosted champagne glass to kill her.

He then tip-toed back to the bathroom, shut the door,
climbed out of the window and back downstairs to his
own apartment.

He remembered to take his garlic press with him, but
stupidly forgot the tooth-glass, which he left on the
bathroom shelf.

PROCESS OF DEDUCTION:

Everyone had a motive:

Mimi Colada was intensely jealous of Lisa May yet they were best of friends and she had an alibi in her doctor.

Tony Delgordo killed Gianni Rimini for Lisa May, with whom he was madly in love. He had reason to kill Lisa May as his love was unrequited but he had an alibi in Clara B. His one-way ticket to Miami made him look guilty, but in truth, he was simply running away because Lisa May threatened to reveal that he had murdered Gianni.

Clara Bensonhurst was obsessed with her former employer but the relationship had been nothing other than professional. She might have wanted to kill Lisa May because she was cross that she had inherited all Gianni's money, which she had wanted for her charities, but she had an alibi in Tony D - and remember, you know the murderer acted alone. Although she didn't think highly of Lisa May, she gave her an expensive bottle of Cristal on her birthday because she didn't want to lose the Rimini business.

Lucy Westerheim has a reputation for ruthlessness and had had to sell her apartment to pay her restaurants' debts, so she could have wanted to kill Lisa May, who had increased the level of interest on her loans. She had been Gianni Rimini's mistress and while he had been alive, he had helped her with her business and turned a blind eye to her late payments. Lisa May however had told her to find $18,000 "or else". Her alibi is dead but she didn't know about the plant - Winford gave Lisa May the plant last month (August) and we know Lucy W. had not been in the apartment since Gianni Rimini's death (July). She was also not lying when she said she hadn't entered the kitchen or the bathroom.

Neither Winford Thurston nor Charles Crowhurst had alibis and either of them could have entered the kitchen at the crucial time.
Not only is **Winford T** a sadist and a junkie but he had been spurned by Lisa May and could easily have wanted to kill her....
BUT
- the FBI transcript of the party revealed that Winford T. had no idea which champagne glass Lisa May preferred.

Further clues:

Arnold Wilson's note to Det Schwarz revealed that neither he nor Clara B. knew of any intention on Lisa May's part to sell, her apartment - yet had Lisa May intended to sell, as Charles C. said, she would have had every opportunity to tell Clara B. when she met her on the night of her murder between 5.00-5.45pm, after speaking with Charles C. between 4.30-4.55pm.

Charles's enthusiastic reference to Tommy Batherd's incredible memory for faces and times was made to establish a cast iron alibi.

The Spiller & Lane report on Charles C. states that he used the fire escape to terrify his elderly neighbours.

The presence of rust in both the champagne glass and the "mixing" glass in the bathroom came from Charles C's hands after he had clambered up the fire escape.

The scraping and slamming noises Mimi heard were caused by Charles C. opening and closing the bathroom window. She also heard him pottering around in the bathroom and noises from the road - heard while the window was open, letting all the cold air in.

The door shutting and footsteps that Winford heard was Charles C. sneaking from the bathroom to the kitchen and back again.